KS2 SATs
Arithmetic
10-Minute Tests

Hilary Koll and Steve Mills

Schofield & Sims

Introduction

This book contains 22 bite-sized tests to give you practice in answering arithmetic questions quickly.

Each test contains 10 questions and is designed to be completed in 10 minutes.

The questions are just like the questions you will need to answer in the SATs Arithmetic paper in Year 6.

What you will need

- a pencil
- an eraser
- a clock, watch or stopwatch
- an adult to time you and to mark the tests for you

How to use the book

Make sure that you are sitting in a quiet place where there aren't any distractions.

Turn to **Test 1** on page 4.

Start by answering the two warm-up questions. These will help to get you ready for the test.

Tell the adult when you have finished. They will start the timer.

Read each question carefully and write the answer. You should not use a calculator.

Work through the questions in order. Try to answer every question. If you get stuck on a question, leave it and move on to the next one. Work quickly and try to do your best.

When you reach the end of the test, stop and tell the adult that you have finished.

The adult will mark your test. Then the adult will fill in the **Total marks** and **Time taken** sections at the end of the test.

Turn to the **Progress chart** on page 48. Write your score in the box and colour the chart to show this score.

If you got some of the questions wrong, have another go at them before you look at the answers. Then ask the adult to check your work and help if you are still not sure.

Published by **Schofield & Sims Ltd**, 7 Mariner Court, Wakefield, West Yorkshire WF4 3FL, UK
Telephone 01484 607080
www.schofieldandsims.co.uk

This edition copyright © Schofield & Sims Ltd, 2019
First published in 2019
Second impression 2020

Authors: **Hilary Koll and Steve Mills**
Hilary Koll and Steve Mills have asserted their moral rights under the Copyright, Designs and Patents Act, 1988, to be identified as the authors of this work.

British Library Cataloguing in Publication Data
A catalogue record for this book is available from the British Library.

Design by **Ledgard Jepson**
Printed in the UK by **DG3**

ISBN 978 0721 71493 6

Contents

Notes for parents, teachers and other adult helpers

A pull-out answers section (pages A1 to A12) appears in the centre of this book, between pages 24 and 25. This provides answers to all the questions, along with guidance on marking the papers. Remove the pull-out section before the child begins working through the tests.

Test 1

Warm-up question	Warm-up question
$492 + 10 =$	$\frac{6}{7} - \frac{3}{7} =$

1 $100 + 721 =$

1 mark

2 $77 \div 11 =$

1 mark

3   ☐ $= 542 + 689$

1 mark

4 $5 - 1.35 =$

1 mark

5 $40 \times 70 =$

1 mark

6 $92 \div 4 =$

1 mark

7 $\frac{7}{10} - \frac{3}{20} =$

1 mark

8 $\frac{4}{5}$ of 30 =

1 mark

9 Show your method.

```
        6  1
  ×     5  7
```

2 marks

10 Show your method.

```
  1  9 | 7  9  8
```

2 marks

Total marks .... Time taken ....

Test 2

Warm-up question	Warm-up question
100 + 994 =	$\frac{11}{12} - \frac{10}{12} =$

1 ☐ + 10 = 1,007

1 mark

2 713 − 20 =

1 mark

3 96 ÷ 8 =

1 mark

4 641 − 52 =

1 mark

5 87 × 9 =

1 mark

6 606 ÷ 1 =

1 mark

7 $\frac{5}{6} - \frac{5}{12} =$

1 mark

8 $5.09 + 6.001 =$

1 mark

9 Show your method.

```
      3  2
×     4  8
```

2 marks

10 Show your method.

```
2  8 | 9  8  0
```

2 marks

Total marks ....   Time taken ....

Test **3**

Warm-up question

$\frac{57}{100} - \frac{32}{100} =$

Warm-up question

$971 + 100 =$

---

1   $7 \times 12 =$

1 mark

2   $327 + 291 =$

1 mark

---

3   $6 - 2.15 =$

1 mark

4   $300 \div 50 =$

1 mark

---

5   $271 \times 4 =$

1 mark

6   $488 \div 4 =$

1 mark

7 20% of 2,400 =

1 mark

8 $\frac{5}{8} \div 5 =$

1 mark

9 Show your method.

		3	6
×		2	9

2 marks

10 Show your method.

4 2 | 7 1 4

2 marks

Total marks ....   Time taken ....

Test 4

Warm-up question	Warm-up question
1,073 − ☐ = 973	49 ÷ 7 = ☐

1 5,375 − 847 =

1 mark

2 ☐ = 47 × 6

1 mark

3 $\frac{5}{9} - \frac{2}{9} =$

1 mark

4 521 × 0 =

1 mark

5 120 ÷ 6 =

1 mark

6 2.8 + 4.027 =

1 mark

7 0.8 ÷ 10 =

1 mark

8 $\frac{1}{5} + \frac{1}{3}$ =

1 mark

9 Show your method.

			7	1	7
×				9	3

2 marks

10 Show your method.

3 3 | 8 2 5

2 marks

Total marks .... Time taken ....

Test **5**

Warm-up question

$496 + 18 =$

Warm-up question

$8 \times 8 =$

---

1 ⬚ $- 10 = 597$

1 mark

2 $927 - 48 =$

1 mark

---

3 $\frac{2}{9} + \frac{5}{9} =$

1 mark

4 $8,800 \div 11 =$

1 mark

---

5 $375 + 2,946 =$

1 mark

6 $756 \div 6 =$

1 mark

7 5% of 1,000 =

1 mark

8 $1\frac{1}{4} - \frac{3}{8} =$

1 mark

9 Show your method.

```
      4 2 3
  ×     4 7
```

2 marks

10 Show your method.

```
1 7 | 8 8 4
```

2 marks

Total marks .... Time taken ....

Test 6

Warm-up question 458 − 19 =	Warm-up question 731 × 0 =

1   720 ÷ 12 =

1 mark

2   [ ] = 62 × 8

1 mark

3   606 + 1,919 =

1 mark

4 $\frac{57}{100} + \frac{32}{100} =$

1 mark

5   438 ÷ 6 =

1 mark

6 $4^2 - 5 =$

1 mark

7 20% × 1,400 =

1 mark

8 2.005 + 8.19 =

1 mark

9 Show your method.

```
      8 3 6
  ×     5 4
```

2 marks

10 Show your method.

```
5 2 | 8 3 2
```

2 marks

Total marks .... Time taken ....

Test 7

Warm-up question

$823 - 40 =$

Warm-up question

$423 \div 1 =$

1   $7 - 2.65 =$

1 mark

2   $168 \times 3 =$

1 mark

3   $\frac{63}{100} - \frac{48}{100} =$

1 mark

4   $90 \div 15 =$

1 mark

5   $574 \div 7 =$

1 mark

6   $0.8 \times 200 =$

1 mark

7 $2\frac{1}{3} + \frac{3}{4} =$

1 mark

8 99% of 400 =

1 mark

9 Show your method.

			6	1	9
×				3	6

2 marks

10 Show your method.

3	6	7	9	2

2 marks

Total marks .... Time taken ....

Test **8**

Warm-up question	Warm-up question
[ ] = 356 + 700	450 ÷ 5 = [ ]

1 $\frac{6}{7} + \frac{6}{7} =$

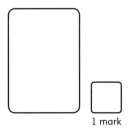

1 mark

2 [   ] = 4907 − 849

1 mark

3 60 × 80 =

1 mark

4 406,040 = 400,000 + [   ] + 40

1 mark

5 384 ÷ 8 =

1 mark

6 $1\frac{2}{5} + \frac{4}{5} =$

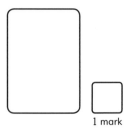

1 mark

7 9.4 – 7.291 =

1 mark

8 15% × 660 =

1 mark

9 Show your method.

			4	8	7
×				6	4

2 marks

10 Show your method.

2 4 ⟌ 9 3 6

2 marks

Total marks .... Time taken ....

Test 9

Warm-up question	Warm-up question
924 + 600 =	3 × 10 × 9 =

1 $\frac{8}{12} + \frac{9}{12} =$

1 mark

2 3,600 ÷ 9 =

1 mark

3 9,070,007 = 9,000,000 + [   ] + 7

1 mark

4 120 × 12 =

1 mark

5 16.98 + 14.215 =

1 mark

6 $\frac{4}{5} + \frac{1}{8} =$

1 mark

7 11% of 240 =

1 mark

8 $\frac{1}{10} \times \frac{5}{8} =$

1 mark

9 Show your method.

```
        8  0  6
  ×        7  5
```

2 marks

10 Show your method.

```
3  4 | 7  8  2
```

2 marks

Total marks .... Time taken ....

Test 10

Warm-up question	Warm-up question
2 × 55 =	4,800 ÷ 6 =

1 ⬜ = 547 + 90

1 mark

2 7,085 − 602 =

1 mark

3 8² + 10 =

1 mark

4 207 ÷ 9 =

1 mark

5 $\frac{6}{7} + \frac{1}{3}$ =

1 mark

6 $\frac{7}{10}$ of 80 =

1 mark

7 2% × 4,300 =

1 mark

8 0.03 ÷ 10 =

1 mark

9 Show your method.

```
        9  1  7
  ×        4  6
```

2 marks

10 Show your method.

```
2  3 │ 3  0  3  6
```

2 marks

Total marks .... Time taken ....

Test 11

1   7 × 33 =

1 mark

2   562 ÷ 1,000 =

1 mark

3   552 ÷ 6 =

1 mark

4   8,327 + 43,099 =

1 mark

5   2.3 × 30 =

1 mark

6 $\frac{3}{8} \times \frac{4}{5}$ =

1 mark

KS2 SATs Arithmetic 10-Minute Tests

Notes for parents, teachers and other adult helpers

KS2 SATs Arithmetic 10-Minute Tests are short, timed tests designed to build speed and fluency.

The questions in the tests closely match the questions children will need to answer in the Key Stage 2 SATs Arithmetic paper, which is taken in Year 6. As children work through the book, the tests get progressively more challenging.

It is intended that children will take around 10 minutes to complete each test.

How to use the book

Remove this pull-out section before giving the book to the child.

Before the child begins work on the first test, together read the instructions on page 2. As you do so, point out to the child that there is a target time of 10 minutes for completing the test.

Make sure the child has all the equipment in the list headed **What you will need** on page 2.

Be sure that the child knows to tell you clearly when they have finished the test.

When the child is ready, say 'Start the test now' and make a note of the start time.

When the child has finished, make a note of the end time and then work out how long they took to complete the test. Then fill in the **Time taken** section, which appears at the end of the test.

Mark the child's answers using this pull-out section. Each test is out of 12 marks. Then complete the **Total marks** section at the end of the test.

Turn to the **Progress chart** on page 48. Encourage the child to write their score in the box and colour the chart to show this score.

Whatever the test score, always encourage the child to have another go at the questions that they got wrong – without looking at the answers. If the child's answers are still incorrect, work through these questions together. Demonstrate the correct method if necessary.

If the child struggles with particular question types (for example, questions involving fractions), help them to develop the skills and strategies needed.

Ask them to complete the next test at a later date, once they have had sufficient time to practise any question types they found difficult.

Answers

Test 1 (page 4)

Warm-up question $492 + 10 = 502$		Warm-up question $\frac{6}{7} - \frac{3}{7} = \frac{3}{7}$	
1 $100 + 721 = 821$	**1 mark**	**2** $77 \div 11 = 7$	**1 mark**
3 $\begin{array}{r} 5\ 4\ 2 \\ +\ \ 6\ 8\ 9 \\ \hline 1\ 2\ 3\ 1 \\ \hline \ _1\ _1\ _1 \end{array}$	**1 mark**	**4** $\begin{array}{r} {}^4\ {}^9 \\ 5.{}^1 0\ {}^1 0 \\ -\ 1.3\ 5 \\ \hline 3.6\ 5 \end{array}$	**1 mark**
5 $40 \times 70 = 4 \times 7 \times 10 \times 10 = 28 \times 100 = 2800$	**1 mark**	**6** $\begin{array}{r} 2\ 3 \\ 4\overline{)9\ {}^1 2} \end{array}$	**1 mark**
7 $\frac{7}{10} - \frac{3}{20} = \frac{14}{20} - \frac{3}{20} = \frac{11}{20}$	**1 mark**	**8** $\frac{4}{5}$ of $30 = 30 \div 5 \times 4 = 6 \times 4 = 24$	**1 mark**
9 $\begin{array}{r} 6\ 1 \\ \times\ \ \ 5\ 7 \\ \hline 4_4 2\ 7 \\ +\ 3_3 0\ 5\ 0 \\ \hline 3\ 4\ 7\ 7 \end{array}$ $\quad \begin{array}{l} 7 \times 61 \\ 50 \times 61 \end{array}$	**Award 2 marks for the correct answer. Otherwise, award 1 mark for correct workings.**	**10** $\begin{array}{r} 4\ 2 \\ 1\ 9\overline{)7\ 9\ 8} \\ -\ 7\ 6 \\ \hline 3\ 8 \\ -\ 3\ 8 \\ \hline 0 \end{array}$	**Award 2 marks for the correct answer. Otherwise, award 1 mark for correct workings.**

Test 2 (page 6)

Warm-up question $100 + 994 = 1094$		Warm-up question $\frac{11}{12} - \frac{10}{12} = \frac{1}{12}$	
1 $997 + 10 = 1007$	**1 mark**	**2** $713 - 20 = 693$	**1 mark**
3 $96 \div 8 = 12$	**1 mark**	**4** $\begin{array}{r} {}^5\ {}^{13} \\ 6.\ 4.\ {}^1 1 \\ -\ \ \ 5\ 2 \\ \hline 5\ 8\ 9 \end{array}$	**1 mark**
5 $\begin{array}{r} 8\ 7 \\ \times\ \ \ \ 9 \\ \hline 7\ 8\ 3 \\ \hline _7\ _6 \end{array}$	**1 mark**	**6** $606 \div 1 = 606$	**1 mark**
7 $\frac{5}{6} - \frac{5}{12} = \frac{10}{12} - \frac{5}{12} = \frac{5}{12}$	**1 mark**	**8** $5.09 + 6.001 = 11.091$	**1 mark**
9 $\begin{array}{r} 3\ 2 \\ \times\ \ \ 4\ 8 \\ \hline 2_2 5_1 6 \\ +\ 1_1 2\ 8\ 0 \\ \hline 1\ 5\ 3\ 6 \\ \hline \ _1 \end{array}$ $\quad \begin{array}{l} 8 \times 32 \\ 40 \times 32 \end{array}$	**Award 2 marks for the correct answer. Otherwise, award 1 mark for correct workings.**	**10** $\begin{array}{r} 3\ 5 \\ 2\ 8\overline{)9\ 8\ 0} \\ -\ 8\ 4 \\ \hline 1\ 4\ 0 \\ -\ 1\ 4\ 0 \\ \hline 0 \end{array}$	**Award 2 marks for the correct answer. Otherwise, award 1 mark for correct workings.**

Test 3 (page 8)

Warm-up question $\frac{57}{100} - \frac{32}{100} = \frac{57 - 32}{100} = \frac{25}{100} = \frac{1}{4}$	Warm-up question $971 + 100 = 1071$

Test 3 (page 8) continued

1 $7 \times 12 = 84$ 1 mark

2
```
    3 2 7
  + 2 9 1
    6 1 8
      1
```
1 mark

3 $6 - 2.15 = 3.85$ 1 mark

4 $300 \div 50 = 30 \div 5 = 6$ 1 mark

5
```
      2 7 1
  ×       4
    1 0 8 4
      1 2
```
1 mark

6 $488 \div 4 = 122$ 1 mark

7 20% of 2400 = 2 × 10% of 2400 = 2 × 240 = 480   1 mark

8 $\frac{5}{8} \div 5 = \frac{1}{8}$ 1 mark

9
```
        3 6
  ×     2 9
    3₃ 2₅ 4    9 × 36
  + 7₁ 2 0      20 × 36
    1 0 4 4
        1
```
Award 2 marks for the correct answer. Otherwise, award 1 mark for correct workings.

10
```
            1 7
  4 2 ) 7 1 4
      − 4 2
        2 9 4
      − 2 9 4
            0
```
Award 2 marks for the correct answer. Otherwise, award 1 mark for correct workings.

Test 4 (page 10)

Warm-up question
1073 − 100 = 973

Warm-up question
49 ÷ 7 = 7

1
```
      ⁴   ⁶
    5 ¹3 ⁷ ¹5
  −   8 4 7
    4 5 2 8
```
1 mark

2
```
      4 7
  ×     6
    2 8 2
    2 4
```
1 mark

3 $\frac{5}{9} - \frac{2}{9} = \frac{3}{9} = \frac{1}{3}$ 1 mark

4 $521 \times 0 = 0$ 1 mark

5 $120 \div 6 = 20$ 1 mark

6 $2.8 + 4.027 = 6.827$ 1 mark

7 $0.8 \div 10 = 0.08$ 1 mark

8 $\frac{1}{5} + \frac{1}{3} = \frac{3}{15} + \frac{5}{15} = \frac{8}{15}$ 1 mark

9
```
          7 1 7
  ×         9 3
    2₂ 1 5₂ 1    3 × 717
  + 6₆ 4₁ 5₆ 3 0    90 × 717
    6 6 6 8 1
```
Award 2 marks for the correct answer. Otherwise, award 1 mark for correct workings.

10
```
            2 5
  3 3 ) 8 2 5
      − 6 6
        1 6 5
      − 1 6 5
            0
```
Award 2 marks for the correct answer. Otherwise, award 1 mark for correct workings.

Test 5 (page 12)

Warm-up question
496 + 18 = 514

Warm-up question
8 × 8 = 64

1 $607 - 10 = 597$ 1 mark

2
```
        ⁸  ¹¹
    9 ₂ ⁷
  −   4 8
    8 7 9
```
1 mark

Answers

3 $\frac{2}{9} + \frac{5}{9} = \frac{7}{9}$ **1 mark**

4 $8800 \div 11 = 800$ **1 mark**

5
```
    3 7 5
  + 2 9 4 6
  ─────────
    3 3 2 1
    ₁ ₁ ₁
```
1 mark

6
```
      1 2 6
  6 ⟌ 7 ¹5 ³6
```
1 mark

7 5% of 1000 = (10% of 1000) ÷ 2 = 100 ÷ 2 = 50   **1 mark**

8 $1\frac{1}{4} - \frac{3}{8} = 1\frac{2}{8} - \frac{3}{8} = \frac{10}{8} - \frac{3}{8} = \frac{7}{8}$ **1 mark**

9
```
        4 2 3
  ×       4 7
  ─────────────
    2₂ 9₁ 6₂ 1      7 × 423
  + 1₁ 6 9₁ 2 0     40 × 423
  ─────────────
    1 9 8 8 1
          ₁
```
Award 2 marks for the correct answer. Otherwise, award 1 mark for correct workings.

10
```
          5 2
  1 7 ⟌ 8 8 4
      − 8 5
      ─────
        3 4
      − 3 4
      ─────
          0
```
Award 2 marks for the correct answer. Otherwise, award 1 mark for correct workings.

Test **6** (page 14)

Warm-up question
458 − 19 = 439

Warm-up question
731 × 0 = 0

1 $720 \div 12 = 60$ **1 mark**

2
```
        6 2
  ×       8
  ─────────
      4 9 6
      ₄ ₁
```
1 mark

3
```
      6 0 6
  + 1 9 1 9
  ─────────
    2 5 2 5
    ₁   ₁
```
1 mark

4 $\frac{57}{100} + \frac{32}{100} = \frac{57 + 32}{100} = \frac{89}{100}$ **1 mark**

5
```
      7 3
  6 ⟌ 4 3 ¹8
```
1 mark

6 $4^2 - 5 = 4 \times 4 - 5 = 16 - 5 = 11$ **1 mark**

7 20% × 1400 = 2 × 10% of 1400 = 2 × 140 = 280   **1 mark**

8 2.005 + 8.19 = 10.195   **1 mark**

9
```
        8 3 6
  ×       5 4
  ─────────────
    3₃ 3₁ 4₂ 4      4 × 836
  + 4₄ 1₁ 8₃ 0 0    50 × 836
  ─────────────
    4 5 1 4 4
          ₁
```
Award 2 marks for the correct answer. Otherwise, award 1 mark for correct workings.

10
```
          1 6
  5 2 ⟌ 8 3 2
      − 5 2
      ─────
        3 1 2
      − 3 1 2
      ───────
            0
```
Award 2 marks for the correct answer. Otherwise, award 1 mark for correct workings.

Test **7** (page 16)

Warm-up question
823 − 40 = 783

Warm-up question
423 ÷ 1 = 423

1 7 − 2.65 = 7 − 2 − 0.65 = 5 − 0.65 = 4.35   **1 mark**

2
```
      1 6 8
  ×       3
  ─────────
      5 0 4
      ₂ ₂
```
1 mark

3 $\frac{63}{100} - \frac{48}{100} = \frac{63 - 48}{100} = \frac{15}{100} = \frac{3}{20}$ **1 mark**

4 $90 \div 15 = 6$ **1 mark**

Answers

Test 7 (page 16) continued

5

$$82 \over 7\overline{)5\ 7\ ^14}$$

1 mark

6 $0.8 \times 200 = 0.8 \times 100 \times 2 = 80 \times 2 = 160$ 1 mark

7 $2\frac{1}{3} + \frac{3}{4} = 2\frac{4}{12} + \frac{9}{12} = \frac{28}{12} + \frac{9}{12} = \frac{37}{12} = 3\frac{1}{12}$ 1 mark

8 99% of 400 = (100% of 400) − (1% of 400) = 400 − 4 = 396   1 mark

9
$$\begin{array}{r} 6\ 1\ 9 \\ \times\ \ \ 3\ 6 \\ \hline 3_3\ 7_1\ 1_5\ 4 \\ +\ 1_1\ 8\ 5_2\ 7\ 0 \\ \hline 2\ 2\ 2\ 8\ 4 \\ {}_1\ \ {}_1 \end{array}$$
6 × 619
30 × 619

Award 2 marks for the correct answer. Otherwise, award 1 mark for correct workings.

10
$$\begin{array}{r} 2\ 2 \\ 3\ 6\overline{)7\ 9\ 2} \\ -\ 7\ 2 \\ \hline 7\ 2 \\ -\ 7\ 2 \\ \hline 0 \end{array}$$

Award 2 marks for the correct answer. Otherwise, award 1 mark for correct workings.

Test 8 (page 18)

Warm-up question
1056 = 356 + 700

Warm-up question
450 ÷ 5 = 90

1 $\frac{6}{7} + \frac{6}{7} = \frac{6+6}{7} = \frac{12}{7} = 1\frac{5}{7}$ 1 mark

2
$$\begin{array}{r} {}^8\ \ {}^9 \\ 4\ ^9\ ^{10}0\ ^17 \\ -\ \ \ 8\ 4\ 9 \\ \hline 4\ 0\ 5\ 8 \end{array}$$
1 mark

3 $60 \times 80 = 6 \times 8 \times 10 \times 10 = 48 \times 100 = 4800$ 1 mark

4 406 040 = 400 000 + 6000 + 40   1 mark

5
$$\begin{array}{r} 4\ 8 \\ 8\overline{)3\ 8\ ^64} \end{array}$$
1 mark

6 $1\frac{2}{5} + \frac{4}{5} = \frac{7}{5} + \frac{4}{5} = \frac{7+4}{5} = \frac{11}{5} = 2\frac{1}{5}$ 1 mark

7
$$\begin{array}{r} {}^3\ \ {}^9 \\ 9.4\ ^{10}0\ ^10 \\ -\ 7.2\ 9\ 1 \\ \hline 2.1\ 0\ 9 \end{array}$$
1 mark

8 $15\% \times 660 = (10\% \times 660) + \frac{1}{2}(10\% \times 660) =$ 66 + 33 = 99   1 mark

9
$$\begin{array}{r} 4\ 8\ 7 \\ \times\ \ \ 6\ 4 \\ \hline 1_1\ 9_3\ 4_2\ 8 \\ +\ 2_2\ 9_5\ 2_4\ 2\ 0 \\ \hline 3\ 1\ 1\ 6\ 8 \\ {}_1\ \ {}_1 \end{array}$$
4 × 487
60 × 487

Award 2 marks for the correct answer. Otherwise, award 1 mark for correct workings.

10
$$\begin{array}{r} 3\ 9 \\ 2\ 4\overline{)9\ 3\ 6} \\ -\ 7\ 2 \\ \hline 2\ 1\ 6 \\ -\ 2\ 1\ 6 \\ \hline 0 \end{array}$$

Award 2 marks for the correct answer. Otherwise, award 1 mark for correct workings.

Test 9 (page 20)

Warm-up question
924 + 600 = 1524

Warm-up question
3 × 10 × 9 = 270

1 $\frac{8}{12} + \frac{9}{12} = \frac{8+9}{12} = \frac{17}{12} = 1\frac{5}{12}$ 1 mark

2 3600 ÷ 9 = 400   1 mark

3 9 070 007 = 9 000 000 + 70 000 + 7   1 mark

4 120 × 12 = 1440   1 mark

5
$$\begin{array}{r} 1\ 6.9\ 8\ 0 \\ +\ 1\ 4.2\ 1\ 5 \\ \hline 3\ 1.1\ 9\ 5 \\ {}_1\ \ {}_1 \end{array}$$
1 mark

6 $\frac{4}{5} + \frac{1}{8} = \frac{32}{40} + \frac{5}{40} = \frac{32+5}{40} = \frac{37}{40}$ 1 mark

Answers

7 11% of 240 = (10% of 240) + (1% of 240) =
24 + 2.4 = 26.4 **1 mark**

8 $\frac{1}{10} \times \frac{5}{8} = \frac{1 \times 5}{10 \times 8} = \frac{5}{80} = \frac{1}{16}$ **1 mark**

9
```
        8 0 6
    ×     7 5
    4₄0 3₃0      5 × 806
  + 5₅6 4₄2 0     70 × 806
    6 0 4 5 0
        1
```
Award 2 marks for the correct answer. Otherwise, award 1 mark for correct workings.

10
```
          2 3
  3 4 | 7 8 2
      − 6 8
        1 0 2
      − 1 0 2
            0
```
Award 2 marks for the correct answer. Otherwise, award 1 mark for correct workings.

Test 10 (page 22)

Warm-up question
2 × 55 = 110

Warm-up question
4800 ÷ 6 = 800

1 637 = 547 + 90 **1 mark**

2
```
      6
    7 ¹0 8 5
  −   6 0 2
    6 4 8 3
```
1 mark

3 8^2 + 10 = 64 + 10 = 74 **1 mark**

4
```
        2 3
  9 | 2  0 ²7
```
1 mark

5 $\frac{6}{7} + \frac{1}{3} = \frac{18}{21} + \frac{7}{21} = \frac{18 + 7}{21} = \frac{25}{21} = 1\frac{4}{21}$ **1 mark**

6 $\frac{7}{10}$ of 80 = 80 ÷ 10 × 7 = 8 × 7 = 56 **1 mark**

7 2% × 4300 = 2 × (1% × 4300) = 2 × 43 = 86 **1 mark**

8 0.03 ÷ 10 = 0.003 **1 mark**

9
```
        9 1 7
    ×     4 6
    5₅ 5₁ 0₄ 2     6 × 917
  + 3₃6 6₂8 0     40 × 917
    4 2 1 8 2
      1   1
```
Award 2 marks for the correct answer. Otherwise, award 1 mark for correct workings.

10
```
            1 3 2
  2 3 | 3 0 3 6
      − 2 3
          7 3
        − 6 9
            4 6
          − 4 6
              0
```
Award 2 marks for the correct answer. Otherwise, award 1 mark for correct workings

Test 11 (page 24)

Warm-up question
5 × 23 = 115

Warm-up question
50 + 1000 = 1050

1 7 × 33 = 231 **1 mark**

2 562 ÷ 1000 = 0.562 **1 mark**

3
```
        9 2
  6 | 5 5 ¹2
```
1 mark

4
```
      8 3 2 7
  + 4 3 0 9 9
    5 1 4 2 6
    1     1 1
```
1 mark

5 2.3 × 30 = 23 × 3 = 69 **1 mark**

6 $\frac{3}{8} \times \frac{4}{5} = \frac{3 \times 4}{8 \times 5} = \frac{12}{40} = \frac{3}{10}$ **1 mark**

7 0.2 ÷ 100 = 0.002 **1 mark**

8
```
      0
    1 ¹2 4 . 6 3
  −   6 1 . 5 0
      6 3 . 1 3
```
1 mark

Test 11 (page 24) continued

9

```
        6 8 7
    ×     4 8
    5₅ 4₆ 9₅ 6    8 × 687
  + 2₂ 7₃ 4₂ 8 0   40 × 687
    3 2 9 7 6
      1     1
```

Award 2 marks for the correct answer. Otherwise, award 1 mark for correct workings.

10

```
            2 1 4
    2 2 ) 4 7 0 8
        − 4 4
          3 0
        − 2 2
            8 8
          − 8 8
              0
```

Award 2 marks for the correct answer. Otherwise, award 1 mark for correct workings.

Test 12 (page 26)

Warm-up question
$85 ÷ 5 = 17$

Warm-up question
$3048 − 1000 = 2048$

1

```
      3 4 1
    ×     6
    2 0 4 6
    2   2
```
1 mark

2 $\frac{3}{4}$ of $2000 = 2000 ÷ 4 × 3 = 500 × 3 = 1500$
1 mark

3 $6 ÷ 3 − 1 = 1$
1 mark

4 $\frac{2}{3} − \frac{1}{6} = \frac{4}{6} − \frac{1}{6} = \frac{3}{6} = \frac{1}{2}$
1 mark

5 $3\,000\,000 + 60\,000 + 6000 = 3\,066\,000$
1 mark

6 $0.06 ÷ 10 = 0.006$
1 mark

7 55% of $460 = (50\% \text{ of } 460) + (5\% \text{ of } 460) =$
$230 + 23 = 253$
1 mark

8 $1\frac{3}{5} − \frac{7}{10} = 1\frac{6}{10} − \frac{7}{10} = \frac{16}{10} − \frac{7}{10} = \frac{16 − 7}{10} = \frac{9}{10}$
1 mark

9

```
        4 7 9
    ×     8 6
    2₂ 8₄ 7₅ 4    6 × 479
  + 3₃ 8₆ 3₇ 2 0   80 × 479
    4 1 1 9 4
      1   1
```

Award 2 marks for the correct answer. Otherwise, award 1 mark for correct workings.

10

```
            1 3 2
    5 1 ) 6 7 3 2
        − 5 1
          1 6 3
        − 1 5 3
            1 0 2
          − 1 0 2
                0
```

Award 2 marks for the correct answer. Otherwise, award 1 mark for correct workings.

Test 13 (page 28)

Warm-up question
$45 × 5 = 225$

Warm-up question
$154 + 1000 = 1154$

1

```
      ⁸    ⁷
    9 ¹0 8 ¹2
    −   6 0 7
      8 4 7 5
```
1 mark

2 $7 × 1 × 9 = 63$
1 mark

3 $120 ÷ 6 = 20$
1 mark

4 $(9 + 3) × 5 = 12 × 5 = 60$
1 mark

5 $\frac{3}{8} + \frac{4}{5} = \frac{15}{40} + \frac{32}{40} = \frac{15 + 32}{40} = \frac{47}{40} = 1\frac{7}{40}$
1 mark

6 $0.4 × 28 = 4 × 28 ÷ 10 = 112 ÷ 10 = 11.2$
1 mark

7 7% of $300 = (1\% \text{ of } 300) × 7 = 3 × 7 = 21$
1 mark

8

```
      2 6 5 . 5 1 0
    +     7 . 9 2 6
      2 7 3 . 4 3 6
              1   1
```
1 mark

Answers

Test 13 (page 28) continued

9
```
        5 2 7 4
    ×       7 3
    1₁ 5 8₂ 2₁ 2    3 × 5274
  + 3₃ 6₁ 9₅ 1₂ 8 0   70 × 5274
    3 8 5 0 0 2
      1   1   1
```
Award 2 marks for the correct answer. Otherwise, award 1 mark for correct workings.

10
```
              2 1 3
    4 2 ) 8 9 4 6
        − 8 4
          5 4
        − 4 2
          1 2 6
        − 1 2 6
                0
```
Award 2 marks for the correct answer. Otherwise, award 1 mark for correct workings.

Test 14 (page 30)

Warm-up question
$96 ÷ 6 = 16$

Warm-up question
$9342 − 1000 = 8342$

1 $960 ÷ 8 = 120$ — **1 mark**

2 $7^2 + 3 = 7 × 7 + 3 = 49 + 3 = 52$ — **1 mark**

3
```
    7 9 9 9 3
  +   6 7 2 1
    8 6 7 1 4
      1 1 1
```
1 mark

4 $\frac{4}{5} − \frac{3}{10} = \frac{8}{10} − \frac{3}{10} = \frac{5}{10} = \frac{1}{2}$ — **1 mark**

5 $0.7 ÷ 100 = 0.007$ — **1 mark**

6 6% of $400 = (1\%$ of $400) × 6 = 4 × 6 = 24$ — **1 mark**

7 $0.6 × 300 = 6 × 30 = 180$ — **1 mark**

8 $\frac{6}{8} ÷ 3 = \frac{6 ÷ 3}{8} = \frac{2}{8} = \frac{1}{4}$ — **1 mark**

9
```
        1 6 5 2
    ×       3 5
    8₃ 2₂ 6₁ 0    5 × 1652
  + 4₁ 9₁ 5 6 0   30 × 1652
    5 7 8 2 0
      1     1
```
Award 2 marks for the correct answer. Otherwise, award 1 mark for correct workings.

10
```
              2 3 2
    3 6 ) 8 3 5 2
        − 7 2
          1 1 5
        − 1 0 8
              7 2
            − 7 2
                0
```
Award 2 marks for the correct answer. Otherwise, award 1 mark for correct workings.

Test 15 (page 32)

Warm-up question
$44 × 7 = 308$

Warm-up question
$\frac{6}{9} + \frac{7}{9} = \frac{6 + 7}{9} = \frac{13}{9} = 1\frac{4}{9}$

1
```
      0  9  10
    1 ¹0 ¹1 ⁷7
  −     8 2 8
        1 8 9
```
1 mark

2
```
          8 9
    8 ) 7 1 ⁷2
```
1 mark

3 $8\,000\,000 + 70\,000 + 9000 = 8\,079\,000$ — **1 mark**

4 $\frac{3}{4} + \frac{3}{8} = \frac{6}{8} + \frac{3}{8} = \frac{9}{8} = 1\frac{1}{8}$ — **1 mark**

5 $9^2 + 3 × 5 = 81 + 15 = 96$ — **1 mark**

6
```
        5  9
    6.¹0 ¹0 3
  − 1.2 5 0
    4.7 5 3
```
1 mark

7 $45\% × 250 = (50\%$ of $250) − (5\%$ of $250) =$
$125 − 12.5 = 112.5$ — **1 mark**

8 $\frac{3}{8} ÷ 2 = \frac{3}{16}$ — **1 mark**

Test 15 (page 32) continued

<table>
<tr><td>

9
```
        7 3 5 4
  ×         2 6
    4₄ 4₂ 1₃ 2₂ 4    6 × 7354
  + 1₁ 4 7₁ 0 8 0    20 × 7354
    1 9 1 2 0 4
      1     1
```
</td><td>

Award 2 marks for the correct answer. Otherwise, award 1 mark for correct workings.
</td><td>

10
```
              3 1 9
  2 3 ⟌ 7 3 3 7
      − 6 9
          4 3
        − 2 3
          2 0 7
        − 2 0 7
                0
```
</td><td>

Award 2 marks for the correct answer. Otherwise, award 1 mark for correct workings.
</td></tr>
</table>

Test 16 (page 34)

Warm-up question

$55 + 407 = 462$

Warm-up question

$\frac{4}{11} + \frac{10}{11} = \frac{14}{11} = 1\frac{3}{11}$

1 $1320 ÷ 11 = (132 ÷ 11) × 10 = 12 × 10 = 120$ **1 mark**

2 $6\,500\,100 = 6\,000\,000 + 500\,000 + 100$ **1 mark**

3
```
   2  15
  3̶ 6̶ .⁴ 1 1
  −   6 5 0 1
    2 9 9 1 0
```
   1 mark

4 $\frac{3}{5} × 140 = 140 ÷ 5 × 3 = 28 × 3 = 84$ **1 mark**

5 $15 × 5.1 = 15 × 5 + 15 × 0.1 = 75 + 1.5 = 76.5$ **1 mark**

6
```
    0  16  12
  1̶ 7̶ 3̶.⁴ 1
  −   8 3 . 7 0
      8 9 . 7 1
```
   1 mark

7 $2\frac{1}{4} − \frac{2}{3} = 2\frac{3}{12} − \frac{8}{12} = \frac{27}{12} − \frac{8}{12} = \frac{19}{12} = 1\frac{7}{12}$ **1 mark**

8 $\frac{4}{7} ÷ 4 = \frac{1}{7}$ **1 mark**

<table>
<tr><td>

9
```
          3 6 8 3
  ×           7 7
    2₂ 5₄ 7₅ 8₂ 1    7 × 3683
  + 2₂ 5₄ 7₅ 8₂ 1 0  70 × 3683
    2 8 3 5 9 1
      1   1
```
</td><td>

Award 2 marks for the correct answer. Otherwise, award 1 mark for correct workings.
</td><td>

10
```
              4 5 3
  2 1 ⟌ 9 5 1 3
      − 8 4
          1 1 1
        − 1 0 5
              6 3
            − 6 3
                0
```
</td><td>

Award 2 marks for the correct answer. Otherwise, award 1 mark for correct workings.
</td></tr>
</table>

Test 17 (page 36)

Warm-up question

$519 − 74 = 445$

Warm-up question

$\frac{5}{6} + \frac{5}{6} = \frac{5+5}{6} = \frac{10}{6} = 1\frac{4}{6} = 1\frac{2}{3}$

1 $630 ÷ 7 = 90$ **1 mark**

2 $11 × 120 = 1320$ **1 mark**

3 $50 − 22 ÷ 11 = 50 − 2 = 48$ **1 mark**

4 $\frac{6}{7} × \frac{1}{21} = \frac{6 ÷ 3}{7} × \frac{1}{21 ÷ 3} = \frac{2}{7} × \frac{1}{7} = \frac{2 × 1}{7 × 7} = \frac{2}{49}$ **1 mark**

5 $1.3 ÷ 100 = 0.013$ **1 mark**

6
```
      5  11 15
  6̶ 2̶ . 6̶ ¹0
  − 1 7 . 7 3
    4 4 . 8 7
```
   1 mark

7 28% of $120 = 3 × (10\% \text{ of } 120) − 2 × (1\% \text{ of } 120) =$
$3 × 12 − 2 × 1.2 = 36 − 2.4 = 33.6$ **1 mark**

8 $3.7 × 40 = 37 × 4 = 148$ **1 mark**

Answers

9
```
      7 5 8 3
  ×        5 8
    6₆ 0₄ 6₆ 6₂ 4    8 × 7583
  + 3₃ 7₂ 9₄ 1₁ 5 0   50 × 7583
    4 3 9 8 1 4
      1       1
```
Award 2 marks for the correct answer. Otherwise, award 1 mark for correct workings.

10
```
          3 0 6
  1 6 ) 4 8 9 6
      − 4 8
        0 9
        −   0
          9 6
        − 9 6
            0
```
Award 2 marks for the correct answer. Otherwise, award 1 mark for correct workings.

Test **18** (page 38)

Warm-up question
$48 + 918 = 966$

Warm-up question
$10 − 4.6 = 5.4$

1 $12 × 5 × 3 = 60 × 3 = 180$ **1 mark**

2 $211427 − 9998 = 211427 − 10000 + 2 = 201429$ **1 mark**

3 $\frac{3}{4}$ of $18000 = 18000 ÷ 4 × 3 = 4500 × 3 = 13500$ **1 mark**

4 $2^2 + 4 × 8 = 2 × 2 + 4 × 8 = 4 + 32 = 36$ **1 mark**

5 $1\frac{1}{12} − \frac{3}{4} = \frac{13}{12} − \frac{9}{12} = \frac{4}{12} = \frac{1}{3}$ **1 mark**

6 22% of $600 = (20\%$ of $600) + (2\%$ of $600) = 120 + 12 = 132$ **1 mark**

7
```
    8  9  9
  9.⁰0 ⁰0 ¹0
− 8.1  8  9
  0.8  1  1
```
1 mark

8 $\frac{7}{10} ÷ 2 = \frac{7}{20}$ **1 mark**

9
```
      6 9 7 6
  ×        6 8
    5₅ 5₇ 8₆ 0₄ 8    8 × 6976
  + 4₄ 1₅ 8₄ 5₃ 6 0   60 × 6976
    4 7 4 3 6 8
      1   1
```
Award 2 marks for the correct answer. Otherwise, award 1 mark for correct workings.

10
```
          2 1 4
  4 3 ) 9 2 0 2
      − 8 6
        6 0
      − 4 3
        1 7 2
      − 1 7 2
            0
```
Award 2 marks for the correct answer. Otherwise, award 1 mark for correct workings.

Test **19** (page 40)

Warm-up question
$763 × 100 = 76300$

Warm-up question
$6.3 = 10 − 3.7$

1 $1440 ÷ 12 = 120$ **1 mark**

2 $\frac{2}{5}$ of $160 = 160 ÷ 5 × 2 = 32 × 2 = 64$ **1 mark**

3 $14 − (7 − 3) = 14 − 4 = 10$ **1 mark**

4 $368127 − 16999 = 368127 − 17000 + 1 = 351128$ **1 mark**

5 4% of $250 = 4 × (1\%$ of $250) = 4 × 2.5 = 10$ **1 mark**

6
```
    6  9  9
  7.⁰0 ⁰0 ¹0
− 6.4  8  7
  0.5  1  3
```
1 mark

7 $\frac{1}{5} ÷ 2 = \frac{1}{10}$ **1 mark**

8 $1\frac{1}{6} − \frac{1}{4} = 1\frac{2}{12} − \frac{3}{12} = \frac{14}{12} − \frac{3}{12} = \frac{11}{12}$ **1 mark**

Test 19 (page 40) continued

9

$$
\begin{array}{r}
8\ 8\ 1\ 7 \\
\times \quad\quad 7\ 9 \\
\hline
7_7\ 9_7\ 3_1\ 5_6\ 3 \\
+\ 6_6\ 1_5\ 7_1\ 1_4\ 9\ 0 \\
\hline
6\ 9\ 6\ 5\ 4\ 3 \\
{\scriptstyle 1\ \ \ \ 1}
\end{array}
$$

9×8817

70×8817

Award 2 marks for the correct answer. Otherwise, award 1 mark for correct workings.

10

$$
\begin{array}{r}
6\ 6\ 2 \\
1\ 3\,\overline{)8\ 6\ 0\ 6} \\
-\ 7\ 8 \\
\hline
8\ 0 \\
-\ 7\ 8 \\
\hline
2\ 6 \\
-\ 2\ 6 \\
\hline
0
\end{array}
$$

Award 2 marks for the correct answer. Otherwise, award 1 mark for correct workings.

Test 20 (page 42)

Warm-up question
$4100 = 3500 + 600$

Warm-up question
$9 - 4.45 = 4.55$

1

$$
\begin{array}{r}
1\ 2\ 7\ 3\ 5\ 5 \\
+\ \quad\ 7\ 2\ 1\ 5 \\
\hline
1\ 3\ 4\ 5\ 7\ 0 \\
{\scriptstyle 1\ \ \ \ 1}
\end{array}
$$

1 mark

2 $1\frac{1}{2} \times 70 = 1 \times 70 + \frac{1}{2} \times 70 = 70 + 35 = 105$

1 mark

3 $6^2 - 36 \div 9 = 36 - 36 \div 9 = 36 - 4 = 32$ **1 mark**

4 $25 \times 4.1 = 25 \times 4 + 25 \times 0.1 = 100 + 2.5 = 102.5$

1 mark

5 $2\frac{1}{5} + 1\frac{1}{6} = 2\frac{6}{30} + 1\frac{5}{30} = 2 + 1 + \frac{6}{30} + \frac{5}{30} = 3\frac{11}{30}$

1 mark

6 $2400 \div 40 = 240 \div 4 = 60$ **1 mark**

7

$$
\begin{array}{r}
{\scriptstyle 0\ \ 11\ \ 9\ \ 9} \\
\cancel{1}\ \cancel{2}.\cancel{0}\ \cancel{0}\,{}^1 0 \\
-\quad 7.2\ 6\ 4 \\
\hline
4.7\ 3\ 6
\end{array}
$$

1 mark

8 8% of 120 = 8 × (1% of 120) = 8 × 1.2 = 9.6 **1 mark**

9

$$
\begin{array}{r}
9\ 4\ 7\ 6 \\
\times \quad\quad 8\ 7 \\
\hline
6_6\ 6_3\ 3_5\ 3_4\ 2 \\
+\ 7_7\ 5_3\ 8_6\ 0_4\ 8\ 0 \\
\hline
8\ 2\ 4\ 4\ 1\ 2 \\
{\scriptstyle 1\ \ 1\ \ \ \ 1}
\end{array}
$$

7×9476

80×9476

Award 2 marks for the correct answer. Otherwise, award 1 mark for correct workings.

10

$$
\begin{array}{r}
1\ 3\ 5 \\
5\ 5\,\overline{)7\ 4\ 2\ 5} \\
-\ 5\ 5 \\
\hline
1\ 9\ 2 \\
-\ 1\ 6\ 5 \\
\hline
2\ 7\ 5 \\
-\ 2\ 7\ 5 \\
\hline
0
\end{array}
$$

Award 2 marks for the correct answer. Otherwise, award 1 mark for correct workings.

Test 21 (page 44)

Warm-up question

$$
\begin{array}{r}
{\scriptstyle 6} \\
6\ \cancel{7}\,{}^1 4\ 3 \\
-\quad 3\ 5\ 1 \\
\hline
6\ 3\ 9\ 2
\end{array}
$$

Warm-up question
$4.15 = 8 - 3.85$

1 $13 \times 27 \times 0 = 0$ **1 mark**

2 $899\,997 + 3571 = 900\,000 + 3571 - 3 = 903\,571 - 3 = 903\,568$ **1 mark**

3 $1\frac{1}{4} \times 40 = 1 \times 40 + \frac{1}{4} \times 40 = 40 + 10 = 50$ **1 mark**

4 $3 \times (4^2 - 1) = 3 \times (16 - 1) = 3 \times 15 = 45$ **1 mark**

5 $\frac{1}{3} + \frac{1}{4} + \frac{1}{6} = \frac{4}{12} + \frac{3}{12} + \frac{2}{12} = \frac{4+3+2}{12} = \frac{9}{12} = \frac{3}{4}$ **1 mark**

6 $15 \times 1.6 = 15 \times 1 + 15 \times 0.6 = 15 + 9 = 24$ **1 mark**

Answers

Test 21 (page 44) continued

7
$$4\,7.0\,6\,0 \;(^{6}\,^{9}\,^{15})$$
$$-\quad 5.0\,9\,1$$
$$\overline{4\,1.9\,6\,9}$$
1 mark

8 37% of 1400 = 4 × (10% of 1400) − 3 × (1% of 1400)
= 4 × 140 − 3 × 14 = 560 − 42 = 518 **1 mark**

9
$$\begin{array}{r} 7\,6\,9\,4 \\ \times \quad\quad 6\,8 \\ \hline 6_6\,1_5\,5_7\,5_3\,2 \\ +\;4_4\,6_4\,1_5\,6_2\,4\,0 \\ \hline 5\;2\;3\;1\;9\;2 \\ {\scriptstyle 1\quad 1} \end{array}$$
8 × 7694
60 × 7694

Award 2 marks for the correct answer. Otherwise, award 1 mark for correct workings.

10
$$\begin{array}{r} 3\;0\;4 \\ 2\,9\,\overline{|8\;8\;1\;6} \\ -\;8\;7 \\ \hline 1\;1 \\ -\quad 0 \\ \hline 1\;1\;6 \\ -\;1\;1\;6 \\ \hline 0 \end{array}$$

Award 2 marks for the correct answer. Otherwise, award 1 mark for correct workings.

Test 22 (page 46)

Warm-up question
$$\begin{array}{r} 8\;6\;1\;9 \\ +\quad 5\;8\;5 \\ \hline 9\;2\;0\;4 \\ {\scriptstyle 1\;\;1\;\;1} \end{array}$$

Warm-up question
$$\begin{array}{r} 1\;3\;7 \\ \times \quad\;\; 5 \\ \hline 6\;8\;5 \\ {\scriptstyle 1\;\;3} \end{array}$$

1 $1\frac{1}{2} \times 49 = 1 \times 49 + \frac{1}{2} \times 49 = 49 + 24.5 = 73.5$ **1 mark**

2 $4^2 - 5 \times 3 + 7 = 16 - 5 \times 3 + 7 =$
$16 - 15 + 7 = 1 + 7 = 8$ **1 mark**

3 $2.5 \times 61 = 2 \times 61 + 0.5 \times 61 = 122 + 30.5 = 152.5$ **1 mark**

4 $3\frac{1}{3} - 1\frac{6}{7} = 3\frac{7}{21} - 1\frac{18}{21} = \frac{70}{21} - \frac{39}{21} = \frac{31}{21} = 1\frac{10}{21}$ **1 mark**

5
$$\begin{array}{r} 3\;6.7\,0\,0 \;(^{6}\,^{9}) \\ -\;1\;5.5\;2\;9 \\ \hline 2\;1.1\;7\;1 \end{array}$$
1 mark

6 71% × 250 = 2 × 71% of 100 + 71% of 50 =
71 + 71 + 35.5 = 177.5 **1 mark**

7 $\frac{5}{8} \div 2 = \frac{5}{16}$ **1 mark**

8 0.17 ÷ 100 = 0.0017 **1 mark**

9
$$\begin{array}{r} 8\;9\;3\;8 \\ \times \quad\quad 7\;6 \\ \hline 5_5\,3_5\,6_2\,2_4\,8 \\ +\;6_6\,2_6\,5_2\,6_5\,6\,0 \\ \hline 6\;7\;9\;2\;8\;8 \\ {\scriptstyle 1} \end{array}$$
6 × 8938
70 × 8938

Award 2 marks for the correct answer. Otherwise, award 1 mark for correct workings.

10
$$\begin{array}{r} 2\;7\;5 \\ 2\,3\,\overline{|6\;3\;2\;5} \\ -\;4\;6 \\ \hline 1\;7\;2 \\ -\;1\;6\;1 \\ \hline 1\;1\;5 \\ -\;1\;1\;5 \\ \hline 0 \end{array}$$

Award 2 marks for the correct answer. Otherwise, award 1 mark for correct workings.

This book of answers is a pull-out section from **KS2 SATs Arithmetic 10-Minute Tests.**

Published by **Schofield & Sims Ltd**, 7 Mariner Court, Wakefield, West Yorkshire WF4 3FL, UK
Telephone 01484 607080
www.schofieldandsims.co.uk

This edition copyright © Schofield & Sims Ltd, 2019
First published in 2019
Second impression 2020

Authors: **Hilary Koll and Steve Mills**
Hilary Koll and Steve Mills have asserted their moral rights under the Copyright, Designs and Patents Act, 1988, to be identified as the authors of this work.

British Library Cataloguing in Publication Data
A catalogue record for this book is available from the British Library.

All rights reserved. No part of this publication may be reproduced, stored in a retrieval system, or transmitted in any form or by any means, electronic, mechanical, photocopying, recording or otherwise, without either the prior permission of the publisher or a licence permitting restricted copying in the United Kingdom issued by the Copyright Licensing Agency Limited.

Design by **Ledgard Jepson**
Printed in the UK by **DG3**

ISBN 978 07217 1493 6

7 $0.2 \div 100 =$

1 mark

8 $124.63 - 61.5 =$

1 mark

9   Show your method.

			6	8	7		
×				4	8		

2 marks

10   Show your method.

| 2 | 2 | 4 | 7 | 0 | 8 |

2 marks

Total marks ....   Time taken ....

Test 12

Warm-up question

$85 \div 5 =$

Warm-up question

$3,048 - 1,000 =$

1   $341 \times 6 =$

1 mark

2   $\frac{3}{4}$ of $2,000 =$

1 mark

3   $6 \div 3 - 1 =$

1 mark

4   $\frac{2}{3} - \frac{1}{6} =$

1 mark

5   $3,000,000 + \boxed{} + 6,000 = 3,066,000$

1 mark

6   $0.06 \div 10 =$

1 mark

7 55% of 460 =

[   ] [ ] 1 mark

8 $1\frac{3}{5} - \frac{7}{10} =$

[   ] [ ] 1 mark

9 Show your method.

```
      4  7  9
×        8  6
```

[   ] [ ] 2 marks

10 Show your method.

```
5 | 1 | 6  7  3  2
```

[   ] [ ] 2 marks

Total marks .... Time taken ....

Test **13**

1   $9,082 - 607 =$

1 mark

2   $7 \times 1 \times 9 =$

1 mark

3   $120 \div 6 =$

1 mark

4   $(9 + 3) \times 5 =$

1 mark

5   $\frac{3}{8} + \frac{4}{5} =$

1 mark

6   $0.4 \times 28 =$

1 mark

7   7% of 300 =

1 mark

8   265.51 + 7.926 =

1 mark

9   Show your method.

```
        5  2  7  4
  ×           7  3
```

2 marks

10   Show your method.

```
  4  2 | 8  9  4  6
```

2 marks

Total marks ....   Time taken ....

Test 14

Warm-up question

$96 \div 6 =$

Warm-up question

$9,342 - 1,000 =$

1 $960 \div 8 =$

1 mark

2 $7^2 + 3 =$

1 mark

3 $79,993 + 6,721 =$

1 mark

4 $\frac{4}{5} - \frac{3}{10} =$

1 mark

5 $0.7 \div 100 =$

1 mark

6   6% of 400 =

1 mark

7 0.6 × 300 =

1 mark

8 $\frac{6}{8} \div 3 =$

1 mark

9 Show your method.

		1	6	5	2
×				3	5

2 marks

10 Show your method.

3 | 6 | 8 | 3 | 5 | 2

2 marks

Total marks ....   Time taken ....

Test 15

Warm-up question

$44 \times 7 =$

Warm-up question

$\frac{6}{9} + \frac{7}{9} =$

---

1  $= 1{,}017 - 828$

1 mark

2 $712 \div 8 =$

1 mark

---

3 $8{,}000{,}000 + 70{,}000 + 9{,}000 =$

1 mark

4 $\frac{3}{4} + \frac{3}{8} =$

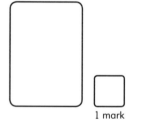

1 mark

---

5 $9^2 + 3 \times 5 =$

1 mark

6 $6.003 - 1.25 =$

1 mark

---

7 45% × 250 =

1 mark

8 $\frac{3}{8} \div 2 =$

1 mark

9 Show your method.

			7	3	5	4	
×					2	6	

2 marks

10 Show your method.

2 3 | 7 3 3 7

2 marks

Total marks .... Time taken ....

Test **16**

1   1,320 ÷ 11 =

1 mark

2   6,500,100 = 6,000,000 +

[   ] + 100

1 mark

3   36,411 − 6,501 =

1 mark

4   $\frac{3}{5} \times 140 =$

1 mark

5   15 × 5.1 =

1 mark

6   173.41 − 83.7 =

1 mark

7 $2\frac{1}{4} - \frac{2}{3} =$

1 mark

8 $\frac{4}{7} \div 4 =$

1 mark

9 Show your method.

			3	6	8	3
×					7	7

2 marks

10 Show your method.

2 1 | 9 5 1 3

2 marks

Total marks ....   Time taken ....

Test **17**

Warm-up question	Warm-up question
519 − 74 =	$\frac{5}{6} + \frac{5}{6}$ =

1 630 ÷ 7 =

1 mark

2 11 × 120 =

1 mark

3 50 − 22 ÷ 11 =

1 mark

4 $\frac{6}{7} \times \frac{1}{21}$ =

1 mark

5 1.3 ÷ 100 =

1 mark

6 62.6 − 17.73 =

1 mark

7 28% of 120 =

1 mark

8 3.7 × 40 =

1 mark

q Show your method.

```
      7  5  8  3
×           5  8
```

2 marks

10 Show your method.

```
1  6 ) 4  8  q  6
```

2 marks

Total marks ....   Time taken ....

Test **18**

Warm-up question

48 + 918 =

Warm-up question

48 + 918 =

Warm-up question

10 − 4.6 =

---

1 12 × 5 × 3 =

1 mark

2 211,427 − 9,998 =

1 mark

3 $\frac{3}{4}$ of 18,000 =

1 mark

4 $2^2 + 4 \times 8 =$

1 mark

5 $1\frac{1}{12} - \frac{3}{4} =$

1 mark

6 22% of 600 =

1 mark

7   9 − 8.189 =

[   ] 1 mark

8 $\frac{7}{10} \div 2 =$

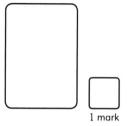

1 mark

9   Show your method.

			6	9	7	6
×					6	8

[   ] 2 marks

10   Show your method.

4 3 ⟌ 9 2 0 2

[   ] 2 marks

Total marks ....   Time taken ....

Test 19

Warm-up question	Warm-up question
763 × 100 =	☐ = 10 – 3.7

1 1,440 ÷ 12 =

1 mark

2 $\frac{2}{5}$ of 160 =

1 mark

3 14 – (7 – 3) =

1 mark

4 368,127 – 16,999 =

1 mark

5 4% of 250 =

1 mark

6 7 – 6.487 =

1 mark

7   $\frac{1}{5} \div 2 =$

1 mark

8   $1\frac{1}{6} - \frac{1}{4} =$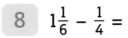

1 mark

q   Show your method.

			8	8	1	7	
×					7	q	

2 marks

10   Show your method.

| 1 | 3 | 8 | 6 | 0 | 6 |

2 marks

Total marks _____   Time taken _____

Test **20**

Warm-up question	Warm-up question
[ ] = 3,500 + 600	9 – 4.45 =
	[ ]

1　127,355 + 7,215 =

[ ]　[ ]

1 mark

2　$1\frac{1}{2}$ × 70 =

[ ]　[ ]

1 mark

3　$6^2 - 36 ÷ 9 =$

[ ]　[ ]

1 mark

4　25 × 4.1 =

[ ]　[ ]

1 mark

5　$2\frac{1}{5} + 1\frac{1}{6} =$

[ ]　[ ]

1 mark

6　2,400 ÷ 40 =

[ ]　[ ]

1 mark

7 12 − 7.264 =

1 mark

8 8% of 120 =

1 mark

9 Show your method.

			9	4	7	6
×					8	7

2 marks

10 Show your method.

5 5 | 7 4 2 5

2 marks

Total marks _____ Time taken _____

Test **21**

Warm-up question	Warm-up question
6,743 – 351 =	$\boxed{}$ = 8 – 3.85

1 13 × 27 × 0 =

1 mark

2 899,997 + 3,571 =

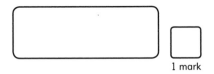

1 mark

3 $1\frac{1}{4} \times 40 =$

1 mark

4 3 × (4² – 1) =

1 mark

5 $\frac{1}{3} + \frac{1}{4} + \frac{1}{6} =$

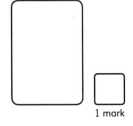

1 mark

6 15 × 1.6 =

1 mark

7 47.06 – 5.091 =

1 mark

8 37% of 1,400 =

1 mark

9 Show your method.

			7	6	9	4
×					6	8

2 marks

10 Show your method.

2	9	8	8	1	6

2 marks

Total marks ....   Time taken ....

Test 22

Warm-up question

8,619 + 585 =

Warm-up question

137 × 5 =

---

1 $1\frac{1}{2} \times 49 =$

1 mark

2 $4^2 - 5 \times 3 + 7 =$

1 mark

3 $2.5 \times 61 =$

1 mark

4 $3\frac{1}{3} - 1\frac{6}{7} =$

1 mark

5 $36.7 - 15.529 =$

1 mark

6 $71\% \times 250 =$

1 mark

7 $\frac{5}{8} \div 2 =$

1 mark

8 $0.17 \div 100 =$

1 mark

q Show your method.

				8	9	3	8	
×						7	6	

2 marks

10 Show your method.

| 2 | 3 | 6 | 3 | 2 | 5 |

2 marks

Total marks .... Time taken ....

Progress chart

Write the score (out of 12) for each test in the box provided to the right of the chart.
Then colour the row next to the box to represent this score.

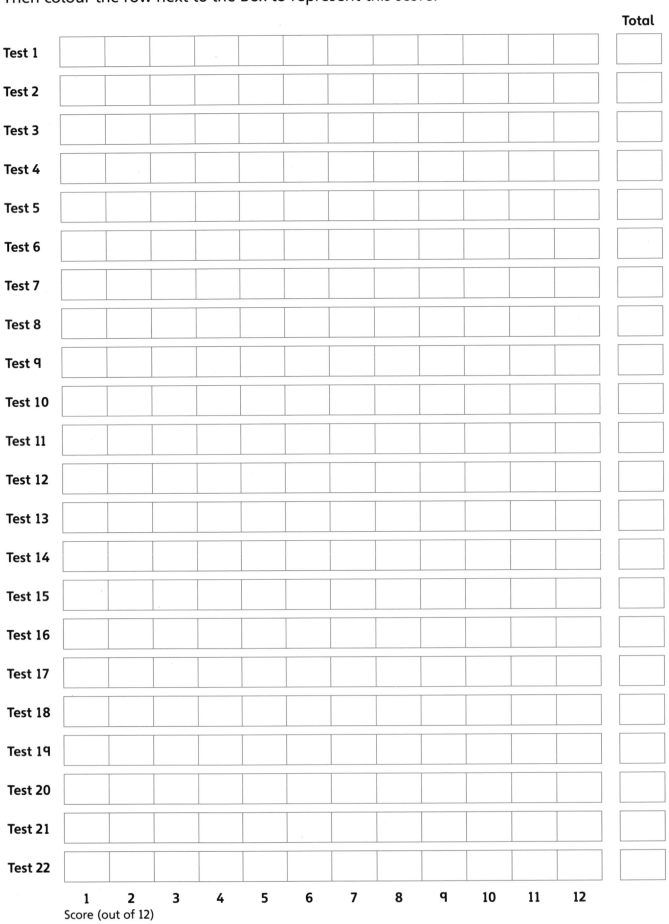

Total

Test 1

Test 2

Test 3

Test 4

Test 5

Test 6

Test 7

Test 8

Test 9

Test 10

Test 11

Test 12

Test 13

Test 14

Test 15

Test 16

Test 17

Test 18

Test 19

Test 20

Test 21

Test 22

1   2   3   4   5   6   7   8   9   10   11   12

Score (out of 12)